Reading Together

The Three Little Pigs

Phonics Consultant: Susan Purcell

Illustrator: Sharon Harmer

Concept: Fran Bromage

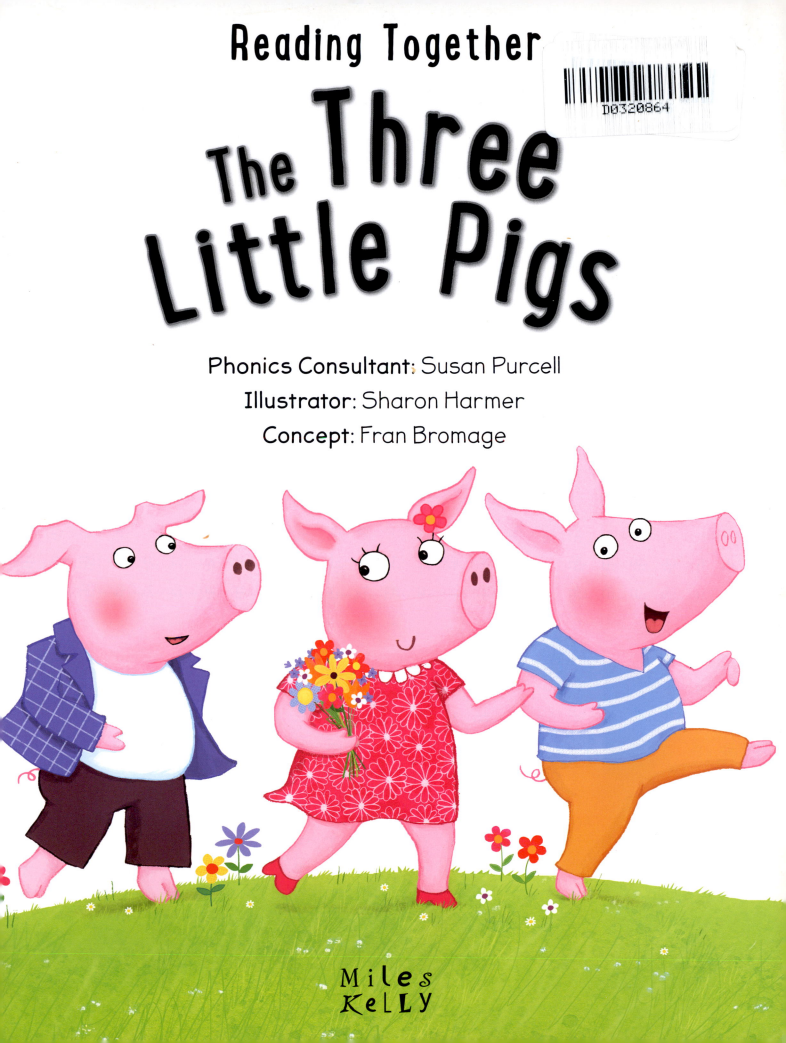

Miles Kelly

Once upon a time, there were three little pink pigs, who lived with their mother, Polly.

Say the names as you spot each pig.

Stick on the pig stickers.

2

Pip

Pat

Pam

One day the little **p**igs, called **P**ip, **P**at and **P**am, **p**acked their bags and left home.

Use your arrow stickers to **point** to the things that are **p**ink.

What a good try! Put a gold star here.

Sound out the things in the picture beginning with **p** as you find them.

petal   **p**ig   **p**ocket   **p**ath

The little pigs laid out a rug in the sun and Pam tucked into a bun. "This is all such fun," she said, "but we must find somewhere to live."

Use your stickers to **spell** some words with the u sound.

bus   hut   nut   run

Just then Pip saw a farmer with a horse and cart full of straw. "I could build a house with that," said Pip. "Do you have any more?"

Caw, caw.

Highlight the or sound (as in horse)

Sound out these words with the **or** sound.

store   chore   adore

jaw   claw   four   pour

Pip built his house of straw, but a hungry wolf thought Pip looked like a tasty tit-bit. "Let me in little pig!" said the wolf.

"Not by the hair on my chinny chin chin. I'll not let you in!" said Pip.

Use your stickers to **complete** this sentence with the **i** sound.

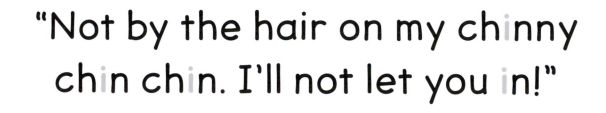

"Not by the hair on my chinny chin chin. I'll not let you in!"

6

"Then I'll huff and I'll puff and I'll blow your house down," boasted the wolf. And he did!

"No, no!" cried Pip, running away. "I must go!"

Sound out these words, which all use the oa sound.

toad   boat   loaf   ago   so

show   low   tow   crow

7

Pat and Pam were **st**ill exploring. Pat found a **st**ack of **st**icks.

"I can build a house with these," he said. "I'll **st**art right now!"

Use your stickers to **spell** some words beginning with **st**.

step   **st**ir   **st**ar   **st**op

Later, Pat heard a tapping at the window. "Let me in little pig!" said the big bad wolf.

"Not by the hair on my chinny chin chin. I'll not let you in," said Pat.

Sound out these words with the a sound in different positions.

tap   cat   flag   that

man   ant   apple

"Then I'll huff and I'll puff and I'll blow your house down," said the wolf with a frown. And he did!

Ow, ow!

Stick on some more words that have the ow sound.

Sound out these words with the ow sound.

cow   brown   town
proud   scout   cloud

10

The wolf sh**ou**ted l**ou**dly as sticks cl**ou**ted his head, and Pat ran **ou**t of the way.

Say the words as you spot the fl**ow**ers.

Stick on the fl**ow**er stickers.

blue fl**ow**ers   yellow fl**ow**ers   red fl**ow**ers

11

Pam was qui**ck** to buy a sta**ck** of bri**ck**s to build her house. She che**ck**ed each wall was strong and thi**ck**.

Use your stickers to **spell** these words, which all use the **k** sound made by **c** and **k**.

sa**ck**   clo**ck**   sti**ck**   tru**ck**

12

"**B**eautiful!" said Pam looking **b**ack at the **b**uilding. "Now I'd **b**etter go inside and unpack my **b**ig **b**ag."

Say the words as you spot things beginning with the **b** sound.

Stick on their stickers.

butterfly

bird

bee

13

Pam sat down with a cup of t**ea** and looked out of the window. She could s**ee** her brothers running past!

"We thr**ee** must fl**ee**," shouted Pip.

Sound out these words with the **ee** sound.

tr**ee**   kn**ee**   fr**ee**

k**ey**   sk**i**   p**ea**   s**ea**

14

Draw attention to the nk ending (as in pink)

Quick as a wi**nk** Pip and Pat told Pam about the wolf.

"Hmm, let me thi**nk**," said Pam, as she dra**nk** some tea. "I thi**nk** I have an idea."

Use you stickers to **spell** some words with the **nk** ending.

pi**nk**   tha**nk**   tru**nk**   bli**nk**

15

Suddenly, the pigs saw the big bad wolf outside in the field. "Let me in little pig!" shouted the wolf.

"Not by the hair on my chinny chin chin. I'll not let you in!" said Pam with a laugh.

"Then I'll huff and I'll puff and I'll blow your house down," said the wolf.

Sound out these words, which all end with the f sound.

graph   leaf   beef

tough   rough   fluff   sniff

So he hu**ff**ed and he pu**ff**ed, and he hu**ff**ed and he pu**ff**ed. Inside, the little pigs were **f**orming a plan.

Use your stickers to **spell** some words beginning with the **f** sound.

face   **f**ootball   **ph**oto   **ph**one

17

"You won't get f**ar**!" shouted the wolf, as he d**ar**ted onto the roof. "You **are** trapped," and he st**ar**ted to climb down the chimney.

Sound out these words with the **ar** sound in different positions.

art   **ar**m   **ar**ch   c**ar**d

d**ar**k   g**ar**den   st**ar**   c**ar**

18

But the sm**a**rt little pigs were on their gu**a**rd. Pam took ch**a**rge of boiling a l**a**rge pot of water under the chimney.

Use your stickers to **spell** more words with the **ar** sound.

j**ar**   h**a**rd   c**ar**t   p**a**rk

Suddenly, the wolf dropped at full **sp**eed into the pot! Water **sp**urted everywhere and **sp**ilt onto the floor.

The wolf gave a ga**sp** of surprise!

Sound out some words beginning with the **sp** sound.

space **sp**in **sp**ot **sp**ell

spend **sp**oon **sp**ade

"Hurrah!" said Pam with a **sp**arkle in her eye. "That's **sp**oilt your plan!"

But the wolf couldn't **sp**eak. He **sp**at out some water and **sp**ed out of the door.

Use your stickers to **spell** more words ending in the **sp** blend.

wa**sp**   cri**sp**   gra**sp**

As you read, focus on the l sound (as in life)

After that, the three pigs lived a lovely life together in Pam's little brick house.

Use your stickers to **spell** some words beginning with l.

leg   lid   leaf   lion

Ask your child to **retell** the story using
these key sounds and story images.

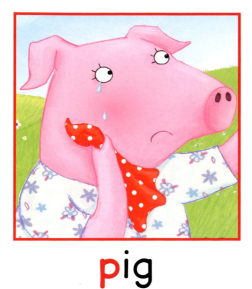
pig

str**aw**

sticks

fr**ow**n

bri**ck**

thi**nk**

hu**ff**

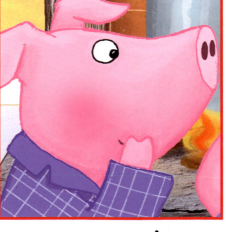
sm**ar**t

spilt

23

Use your stickers to **add** a word that matches
the highlighted **sounds** in each box.

r**u**n   b**u**s   f**u**n   ☐

h**i**s   p**i**g   b**i**t

sh**ow**   t**oa**d   bl**ow**

t**a**p   fl**a**g   **a**pple

bird   **b**ee   **b**ag

s**ea**   kn**ee**   k**e**y

field   tou**gh**   pu**ff**

arm   st**a**r   c**a**rt

lid   **l**eaf   **l**ittle

You've had fun with phonics! Well done.